Copyright © 1989 World International Limited.
All rights reserved throughout the world.
Published in Great Britain by Beaver Publishing Limited,
Orchard Green, Alderley Edge, Cheshire SK9 7DT
Printed in Belgium
ISBN 1 85962 003 5
5th reprint 1997

THE STORY OF
OUR
BABY

written by Brenda Apsley

illustrated by Maureen Galvani

BEAVER PUBLISHING LIMITED

ARRIVAL

put the baby's birth certificate here

ARRIVAL

This book belongs to _____

Born on _____ at _____ am/pm

At _____

Doctor/Midwife _____

Weight _____

Length _____

Colour of eyes _____

Colour of hair _____

YOUR BABY'S FAMILY TREE

Great grandfather

Great grandfather

Great grandmother

Great grandmother

Grandfather

Grandmother

Father

Baby _____

Great grandfather

Great grandfather

Great grandmother

Great grandmother

Grandfather

Grandmother

Mother

Sisters _____   Brothers _____

HOME FROM HOSPITAL

On _____

At _____

put your baby's photographs here

CONGRATULATIONS

First visitors _____

_____

_____

Cards _____

_____

_____

Gifts _____

_____

_____

Flowers _____

_____

_____

BABY FIRSTS

Focuses on parents _____

Smiles _____

Recognizes parents' voices _____

Laughs _____

Holds a toy _____

Claps _____

Recognizes own name _____

Recognizes him/herself in mirror _____

Other important firsts _____

_____

_____

BABY FINGERS – BABY TOES!

Draw around your baby's hand and foot to remind you just how tiny he or she once was!

Hold your baby's hand and foot flat on the page, and draw around them with a pencil. Ink in the outline later.

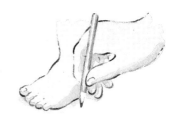

hand print   *foot print*

Date _____   Age _____

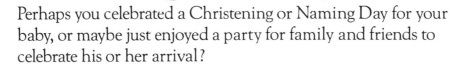

A SPECIAL DAY

Perhaps you celebrated a Christening or Naming Day for your baby, or maybe just enjoyed a party for family and friends to celebrate his or her arrival?

Date _____ At _____

put photographs here

A SPECIAL DAY

Guests _____

_____

_____

_____

_____

_____

Gifts _____

_____

_____

_____

put photographs here

WEIGHTS

Record your baby's weight each month on this chart.

Birth _____

1 month _____

2 months _____

3 months _____

4 months _____

5 months _____

6 months _____

7 months _____

8 months _____

9 months _____

10 months _____

11 months _____

1 year _____

13 months _____

14 months _____

15 months _____

16 months _____

17 months _____

18 months _____

19 months _____

20 months _____

21 months _____

22 months _____

23 months _____

2 years _____

AND MEASURES

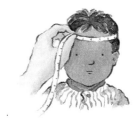

Record your baby's length/height each month on this chart.

Birth _____

1 month _____

2 months _____

3 months _____

4 months _____

5 months _____

6 months _____

7 months _____

8 months _____

9 months _____

10 months _____

11 months _____

1 year _____

13 months _____

14 months _____

15 months _____

16 months _____

17 months _____

18 months _____

19 months _____

20 months _____

21 months _____

22 months _____

23 months _____

2 years _____

ON THE MOVE 1

Record the date when your baby first:

Turns over _____

Rolls on to back _____

Sits when held _____

Sits alone _____

Crawls _____

put photographs here

ON THE MOVE 2

Record the date when your baby first:

Climbs to a standing position _____

Walks with hands held _____

Takes his or her first step _____

Climbs stairs _____

Walks alone _____

put photographs here

MEDICAL RECORDS

You may think that you'll never forget your baby's first immunization, but you will! Fill in dates here so that you have a useful permanent record.

Immunization   Date

_____   _____

_____   _____

_____   _____

_____   _____

_____   _____

_____   _____

_____   _____

MEDICAL RECORDS

Record useful medical details here.

Blood group _____

NHS number _____

Allergies _____

Illnesses _____

_____

_____

_____

Other medical notes _____

_____

_____

MORE BABY FIRSTS

Animal noise _____

Word _____

Name _____

Haircut on _____

FAVOURITE THINGS

Song _____

Book _____

Toy _____

Food _____

TOOTH CHART

Babies cut 20 milk teeth. Record their arrival here. Fill in the date when each tooth appears and mark the sequence on the diagram.

1 _____
2 _____
3 _____
4 _____
5 _____
6 _____
7 _____
8 _____
9 _____
10 _____
11 _____
12 _____
13 _____
14 _____
15 _____
16 _____
17 _____
18 _____
19 _____
20 _____

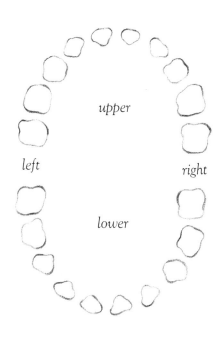

upper

left　　　*right*

lower

FIRST BIRTHDAY

Date _____

Guests _____

_____

_____

_____

put photographs here

FIRST BIRTHDAY

See how your baby has grown in his or her first year. Record a hand and foot outline drawn on his or her first birthday.

foot print   *hand print*

FIRST CHRISTMAS

Date _____

Guests _____

_____

_____

_____

Gifts _____

_____

_____

_____

First snow _____

FIRST CHRISTMAS

put photographs here

FIRST HOLIDAY

Date _____

Place _____

With _____

_____

First paddle _____

First sandcastle _____

put photographs here

FIRST HOLIDAY

put photographs here